FUN AND GAMES with the RECORDER

TUNE 2 BOOK

Method for descant recorder

Gerhard Engel • Gudrun Heyens

Konrad Hünteler • Hans-Martin Linde

Translated and adapted by Peter Bowman

With illustrations by Julie Beech and John Minnion

SCHOTT
EDUCATIONAL
PUBLICATIONS

Contents

About the tunes

Tunes **1** to **7** use all of the notes learned
in **Tutor Book 1** – B, A, G, E, C, and D.

Tunes **8** to **14** use the new note low **D**.

Tunes **16** to **23** use the new notes low **C** and low **F**.

Tunes **25**, **26** and **28** use the new note high **E**.

Tune **29** uses the new note high **F**.

Tunes **30** to **33** use the new note **B** flat.

Tunes **35** to **39** use all of the notes learned
in **Tutor Book 1** and **Tutor Book 2**.

The first recorder part for each tune is always
suitable for the student to play, but the second,
third and fourth parts are sometimes more difficult.
Tunes **6**, **7**, **25**, **26**, **38** and **39** use notes learned
in **Tutor Book 3** whilst tunes **24**, **31**, **33** and **34**
use other members of the recorder family including
the treble, tenor and bass instruments.

The pieces use conventional bar numbering starting
with 1 for the first full bar.

 This symbol is used to indicate a piece
which has a *piano* accompaniment
in the **Insert**.

 This symbol is used on those pieces
which use *guitar chords* to provide
an accompaniment.

ED 12593
British Library Cataloguing-in-Publication Data.
A catalogue record for this book is available from the British
Library.
ISMN M-2201-1912-5
© 1999 Schott & Co. Ltd, London
Material adapted from ED 7772 and ED 7773 © 1990 Schott
Musik International, Mainz, Germany.

Cover, pages 1 and 32 illustrations Julie Beech
All other illustrations John Minnion
Design The Design Works, Reading
Music setting Halstan & Co.

1 Vocalise

Gudrun Heyens

2 Music with a drum

Gerhard Engel

3 Mary-Anne

German folk song
Setting: Gudrun Heyens

Descant recorder 1

Descant recorder 2

Descant (or treble) recorder

4 Oh, when the Saints

Spiritual
Setting: Fritz Emonts

Oh, when the Saints_____ go march-ing in,_____ oh, when the

Saints go march-ing in,_____ then, Lord let me be in that

num-ber_____ oh, when the Saints go march-ing in._____

5 Long balloon journey

Rainer Mohrs

6 Canario

Joachim von dem Hofe
1612

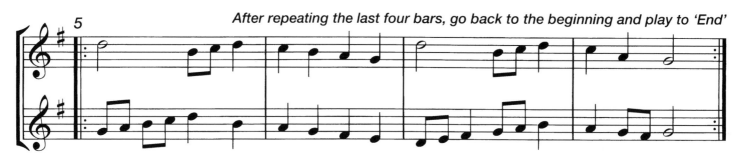

After repeating the last four bars, go back to the beginning and play to 'End'

7 Gavotte (duet)

Michael Praetorius (1571/72-1621)
Setting: Hans-Martin Linde

8 The mill

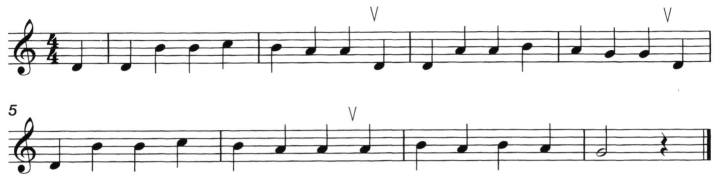

9 Like a Chorale

Gudrun Heyens

7

10 Linear counterpoint in four-four time

Hans-Martin Linde

11 Merrily

Gudrun Heyens

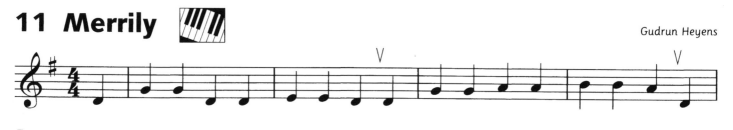

12 Red River Valley

From America
Setting: Matthew Moore

From this val - ley they say you are go - ing,_____ I will
miss your bright eyes and sweet smile_____ For they
say you are tak - ing the sun - shine_____ That
bright - ens our path - way a - while._____

13 Cuckoo

Franz J. Giesbert

From: *Schule des Zusammenspiels*, Schott ED 5585

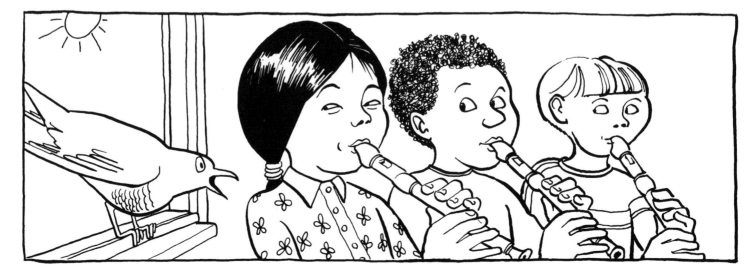

14 Nobody knows

Spiritual
Setting: Hans-Martin Linde

No - bo - dy knows the trou - ble I've seen, no - bo - dy knows but

Je - sus; no - bo - dy knows the trou - ble I've seen,

Fine

Glo - ry Hal - le - lu - ia. Some - times I'm up some - times I'm down,

D.C. al Fine

oh, yes Lord! Some - times I'm al - most to the ground. Oh, yes Lord! Oh,

15 Gilotte

Michael Praetorius
Setting: Hans-Martin Linde

16 Lullaby

16th Century
Setting: Hans-Martin Linde

17 Dance in three-four time

Hans-Martin Linde

Descant recorder 1
Lively

Descant recorder 2

Fine

D.C. al Fine

18 Dance

Hans-Martin Linde

19 Bitoljka

Serbian folk dance
Setting: Hans-Martin Linde

Descant recorder 1

Fast

Descant recorder 2

Descant recorder 3

20 Felisa tiene una potra

Spanish folk song
Setting: Hans-Martin Linde

Flowing

21 Prelude and Canon

Hans-Martin Linde

Descant recorder 1

Calmly

Descant recorder 2

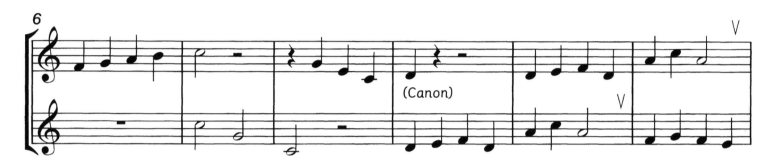

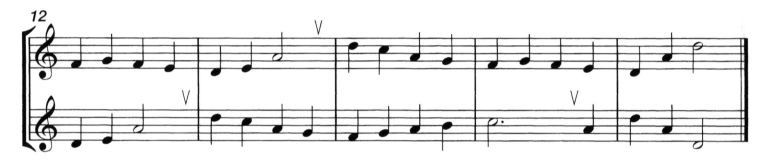

(Canon)

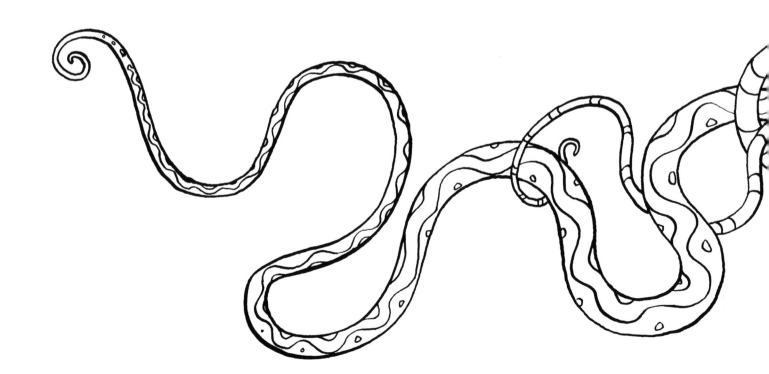

22 Canon

Hans-Martin Linde

Descant recorder 1

Solemnly but not too slowly

Descant recorder 2

23 Triads

Descant recorder 1

Descant recorder 2

Descant recorder 3

Gerhard Engel

24 Little dance

Gerhard Engel

You could add the following percussion rhythm:

25 Dance tune

From an Old Duet Book (1740)

Descant recorder 1

Descant recorder 2

26 Bella Bimba

Italian dance
Setting: Willi Drahts

Descant recorder 1

Descant recorder 2

Descant recorder 3

Tambourine

27 Russian folk song

Setting: Willi Drahts

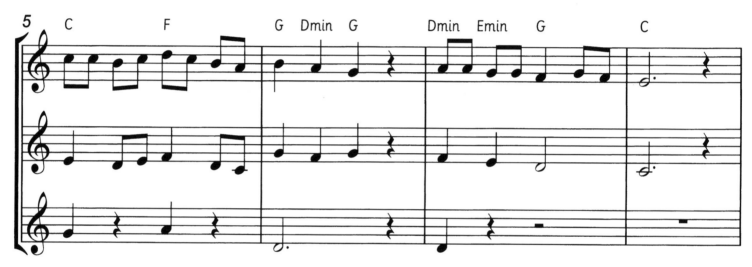

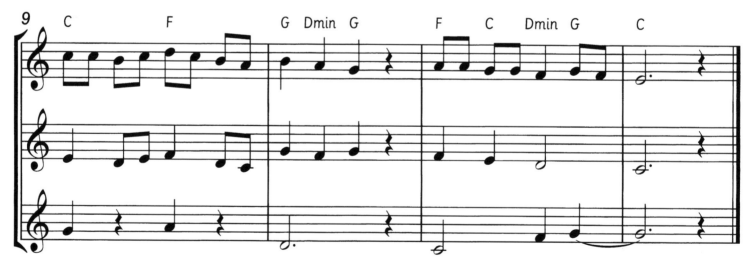

28 The Knights of the Round Table

Setting: Hans-Martin Linde

Descant recorder 1

(Play only on the repeat)

Descant recorder 2

Descant recorder 3

Descant recorder 4

29 Mir han e neue Oberkeet*

after Johann Sebastian Bach (1685-1750)
Setting: Hans-Martin Linde

* 'We have a new overlord' (from the *Peasant Cantata*)

30 Russka

Anikó Baberkoff

31 Gavotte (trio)

George Frideric Handel (1685-1759)

Descant recorder

Treble recorder

Tenor recorder

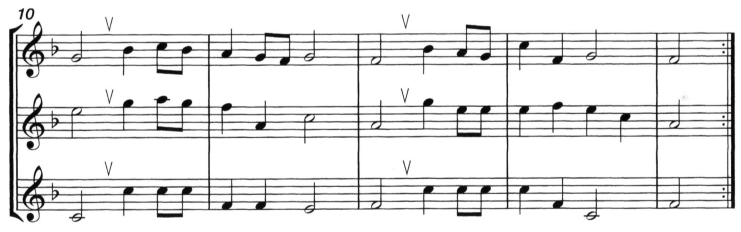

32 Brahms' 'Lullaby'

Johannes Brahms (1833-1897)

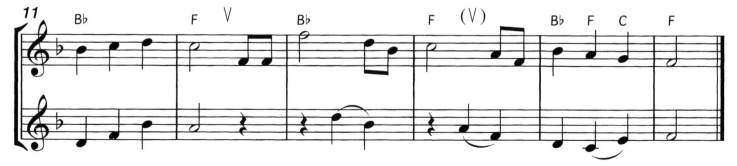

From: *Der Flötenmusikant 1*, Schott ED 3589

33 Hungarian song

Setting: Harald Genzmer

Descant recorder

Andante

Treble recorder

6

11

16

poco rit.

21

a tempo

34 Bransle

Pierre Attaignant (1530)

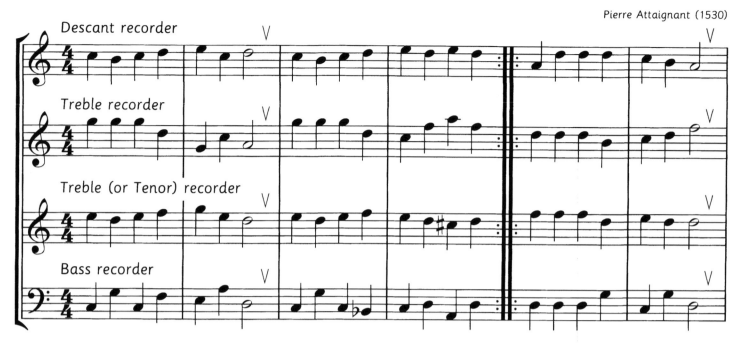

35 Il est né, le divin enfant

French Christmas carol

36 I saw three ships

I saw three ships come sail - ing by, sail - ing by, sail - ing by. I

saw three ships come sail - ing by__ on Christ - mas Day in the morn - ing.

37 Away in a manger

Melody: W. J. Kirkpatrick (1838-1921)
Setting: Walter Bergmann

A - way in a_ man - ger, no_ crib for a bed, the_
The stars in the_ bright sky looked down where he lay, the_

lit – tle Lord Je - sus laid_ down his sweet head.
lit – tle Lord Je - sus a - — sleep on the hay.

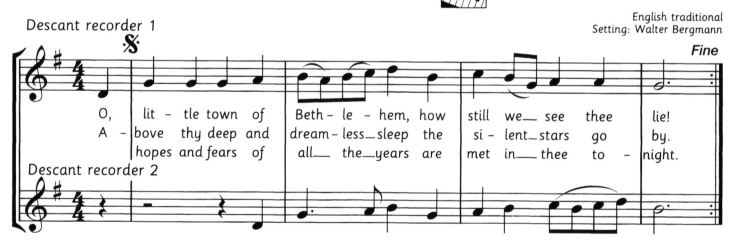

38 O, little town of Bethlehem

English traditional
Setting: Walter Bergmann

Descant recorder 1

Fine

O, lit – tle town of Beth - le - hem, how still we_ see thee lie!
A - bove thy deep and dream - less_ sleep the si - lent_ stars go by.
hopes and fears of all_ the_ years are met in_ thee to - night.

Descant recorder 2

Dal 𝄋 al Fine

Yet_ in thy dark streets shin – eth the e - ver last-ing light; the

39 God rest you merry, gentlemen

English traditional
Setting: Walter Bergmann

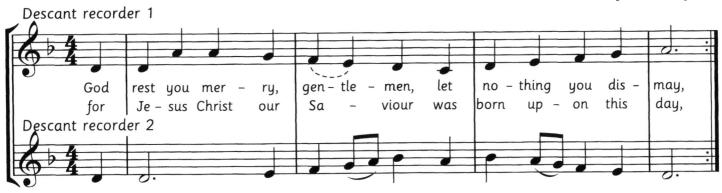

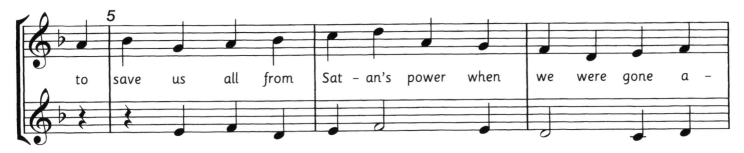

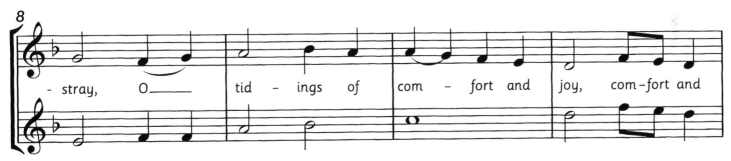

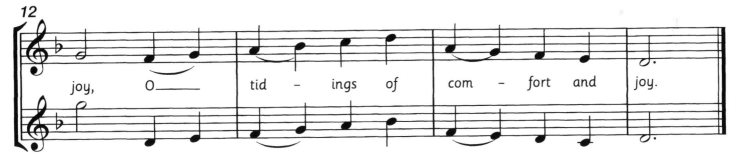

From: *10 Carols to Sing and Play*, ED 10736

Index of tunes

Goodbye everyone! I hope you've had lots of fun. I look forward to seeing you again in **Tune Book 3** of **Fun and Games with the Recorder**.

FUN AND GAMES
with the
RECORDER

TUNE 2 BOOK

PIANO ACCOMPANIMENT
INSERT

Method for descant recorder

ED 12593-01

SCHOTT
EDUCATIONAL
PUBLICATIONS

Contents

ED 12593-01

British Library Cataloguing-in-Publication Data.
A catalogue record for this book is available from the
British Library.

ISMN M-2201-1912-5

© 1999 Schott & Co. Ltd, London

Illustrations Julie Beech

1 Vocalise

Gudrun Heyens

4 Oh, when the Saints

Spiritual
Setting: Fritz Emonts

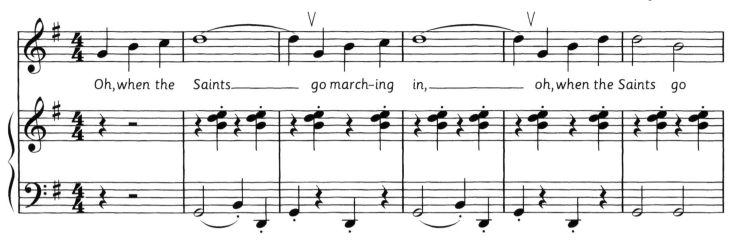

Oh, when the Saints_____ go march-ing in,_____ oh, when the Saints go

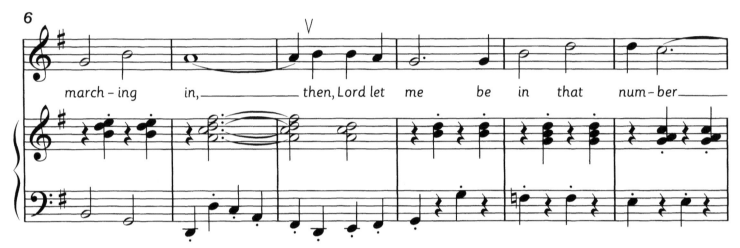

march-ing in,_____ then, Lord let me be in that num-ber_____

_ oh, when the Saints go march - ing in._____

5 Long balloon journey

Rainer Mohrs

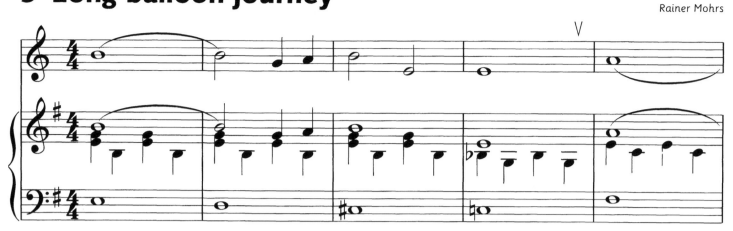

7 Gavotte (duet)

Michael Praetorius (1571/72-1621)
Setting: Hans-Martin Linde

Descant recorder 1

Descant recorder 2

9 Like a Chorale

Gudrun Heyens

11 Merrily

Gudrun Heyens

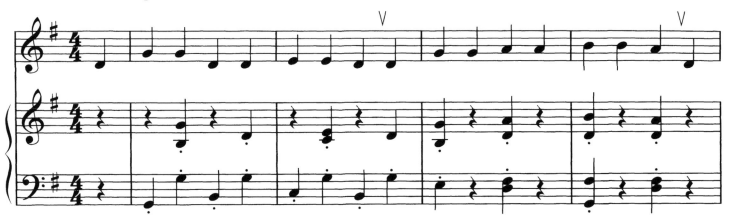

Finish

From the beginning to 'Finish'

12 Red River Valley

From America
Setting: Matthew Moore

From this val – ley they say you are go – ing,_____

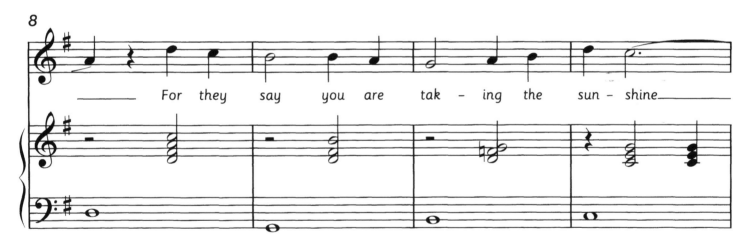

_____ I will miss your bright eyes and sweet smile_____

_____ For they say you are tak – ing the sun – shine_____

_____ That bright – ens our path – way a – while._____

© B. Schott's Söhne, Mainz, 1990

9

14 Nobody knows

Spiritual
Setting: Hans-Martin Linde

Nobody knows the trouble I've seen, nobody knows but

Jesus; nobody knows the trouble I've seen,

Fine

Glory Halleluia. Sometimes I'm up sometimes I'm down,

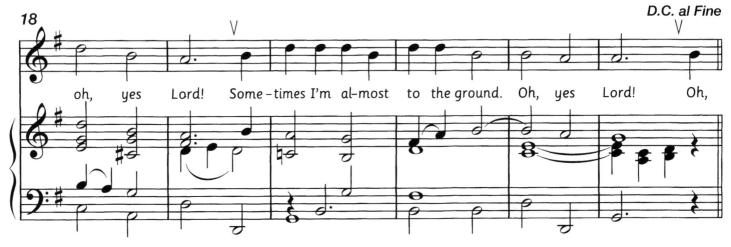

D.C. al Fine

oh, yes Lord! Sometimes I'm almost to the ground. Oh, yes Lord! Oh,

© 1999 Schott & Co. Ltd, London

10

15 Gilotte

Michael Praetorius
Setting: Hans-Martin Linde

16 **Lullaby**

16th Century
Setting: Hans-Martin Linde

20 Felisa tiene una potra

Spanish folk song
Setting: Hans-Martin Linde

Flowing

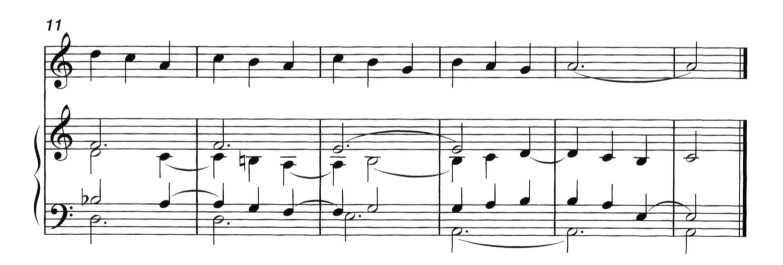

29 Mir han e neue Oberkeet*

after Johann Sebastian Bach (1685-1750)
Setting: Hans-Martin Linde

* 'We have a new overlord' (from the *Peasant Cantata*)

30 Russka

Anikó Baberkoff

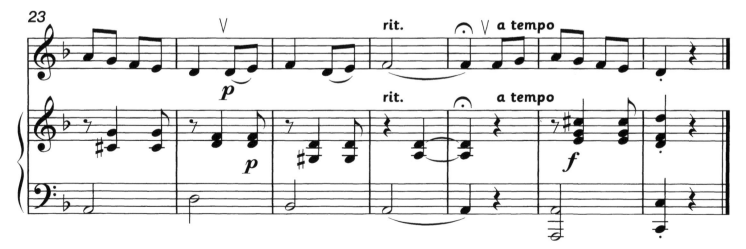

15

Christmas carols

37 Away in a manger

Melody: W.J. Kirkpatrick (1838-1921)
Setting: Walter Bergmann

© 1960 Schott & Co. Ltd, London
From: *10 Carols to Sing and Play*, ED 10736

Away in a manger, no crib for a bed,

The little Lord Jesus laid down his sweet head;

The stars in the bright sky looked down where he lay,

The little Lord Jesus asleep on the hay.

38 O, little town of Bethlehem

English traditional
Setting: Walter Bergmann

O, little town of Bethlehem how still we see thee lie!

Above thy deep and dreamless sleep the silent stars go by.

Yet in thy dark streets shineth the everlasting light;

The hopes and fears of all the years are met in thee tonight.

39 God rest you merry, gentlemen

English traditional
Setting: Walter Bergmann

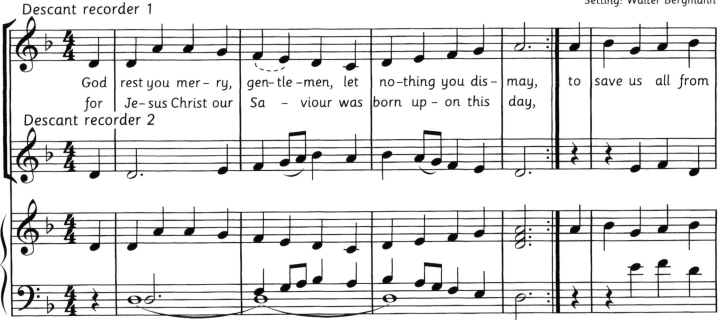

Descant recorder 1

God rest you mer - ry, gen-tle-men, let no-thing you dis - may, to save us all from
for Je-sus Christ our Sa - viour was born up - on this day,

Descant recorder 2

Sat - an's power when we were gone a - stray, O___ tid - ings of com - fort and

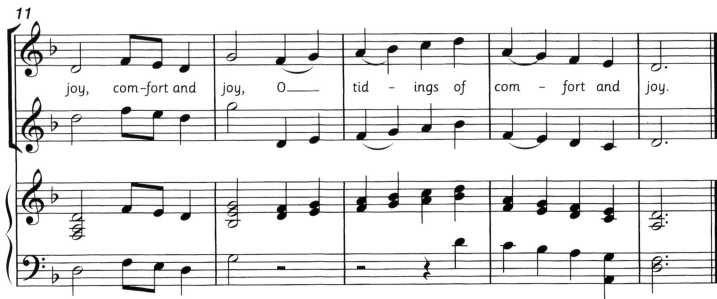

joy, com-fort and joy, O___ tid - ings of com - fort and joy.

From: *10 Carols to Sing and Play*, ED 10736

Index of tunes